The Parable of the Ten Bridesmaids

Matthew 25:1–13 for Children

Written by Claire Miller
Illustrated by Janet McDonnell

CONCORDIA PUBLISHING HOUSE · SAINT LOUIS

"Oh, Jesus," His disciples asked,
"When will the world end? When?
How will we know the time is near
For You to come again?"

"The end will be a big surprise,"
Said Jesus with a smile.
"Be ready—it might happen soon
Or take a long, long while."

"I'll tell a story," Jesus said,
"To help you understand.
It's all about a wedding feast
That happened in our land . . ."

Ten bridesmaids were invited
To a wedding feast one night.
They had to wait outside until
The bridegroom was in sight.

They brought some fiery torches,
For the sun had long gone down.
Oil kept the torches glowing
As they walked through the dark town.

Five bridesmaids did a wise thing:
They brought extra oil along.
The other five were foolish:
You'll soon learn where they went wrong.

The foolish bridesmaids brought no oil.
What could they have been thinking?
The wait was long, all ten were tired,
And soon their eyes were blinking.

The droopy bridesmaids, one by one,
Sat down and fell asleep.
At midnight sharp, a shout rang out.
It made the bridesmaids leap.

"The bridegroom's coming! Hurry!
Trim your torches! Run to greet him!"
The foolish bridesmaids' torches
Were too dim—they couldn't meet him.

"Uh-oh, we need more oil,"
They told the others impolitely.
"So give us some of yours,
Because your lights are shining brightly."

"No, no," the wise ones said,
"There's not enough for us and you.
You'd better buy some oil
And join the party when you're through."

The foolish bridesmaids searched for oil
And finally found some, but
The rest went to the wedding feast,
And then the door was shut.

At last the foolish bridesmaids came
And whined, "They didn't wait!"
They pounded on the door, but heard,
"We're sorry; you're too late!"

Then Jesus told His followers,
"Keep watch and be prepared.
You don't know when the world will end.
Be ready—don't be scared."

Now, how can YOU be ready
For the day the world will end
Or for the day that Jesus calls,
"Come be with Me, My friend"?

Believe that Jesus died for you.
His love's the greatest prize.
And let His light shine in your life,
Like bridesmaids who were wise.

Tell others all about Him
So they'll be ready too.
God's party will be waiting
In His heavenly home for you!

Dear Parents,

This parable is about being ready for the final, joyous coming of Jesus, just as the wise bridesmaids were ready with torches to light their way to the wedding celebration. Jesus is coming again to make all things new. Because He loves us, we wait for Him with excited expectation. This is a joyful parable for Christians: those who have the flame of faith will be counted among the ready.

How can you and your child continue to be prepared and remain in the faith? You can put yourselves in the places where God strengthens your faith. As your child grows, bedtime and meals are natural occasions to discuss Christian living and Bible stories, along with saying prayers of thanksgiving and praise and requesting forgiveness and a stronger faith. Living in God's community of faith—a worshiping congregation—is another important way to place your child in God's hands. Also, involve your child in service activities, such as spreading God's love while feeding the hungry and helping others in need.

As you read this book with your child, point out that the torches were long poles with oil-soaked rags on top. When the bridesmaids trimmed their torches, they cut off the charred edges of the rags and added more oil to keep them burning brightly. They would have carried just enough oil to replenish that one torch.

Therefore, the foolish bridesmaids represent the unprepared. They resist or reject the Word, or they may intend to become active Christians someday when they're not so busy. Jesus' closing words, "Watch therefore, for you know neither the day nor the hour" (Matthew 25:13), are a powerful reminder to those who delay.

More than likely, you won't be around at the end of your child's life. Now is the time to model a life of faith and to pray that your child will remain faithful and ready until the hour comes.

The Author